Dedicated to
Teaghan, James, Rushton, and Hazel

ISBN: 978-0-578-30064-1

www.LSWatercolor.com

Linda Swindle Books
First Edition 2021

Moo, Cow, MOO!

LINDA SWINDLE

Linda Swindle

New, cow, new!

Chew, cow, chew!

Two, cow, two!

Hoo, cow, hoo!

Woo, cow, woo!

A few, cow, a few!

Poo, cow, poo!

The zoo, cow, the zoo!

THE ZOO

Ewe, cow, ewe!

Shoe, cow, shoe!

Blew, cow, blew!

Blue, cow, blue!

Coo, cow, coo!

Emu, cow, emu!

Peek-a-boo, cow, peek-a-boo!

Cockadoodle-doo, cow, cockadoodle-do!

Canoe, cow, canoe!

Tutu, cow, tutu!

Ewww, cow, ewww!

The view, cow, the view!

Hairdo, cow, hairdo!

The crew, cow, the crew!

Moo, cow, moo!

The end!

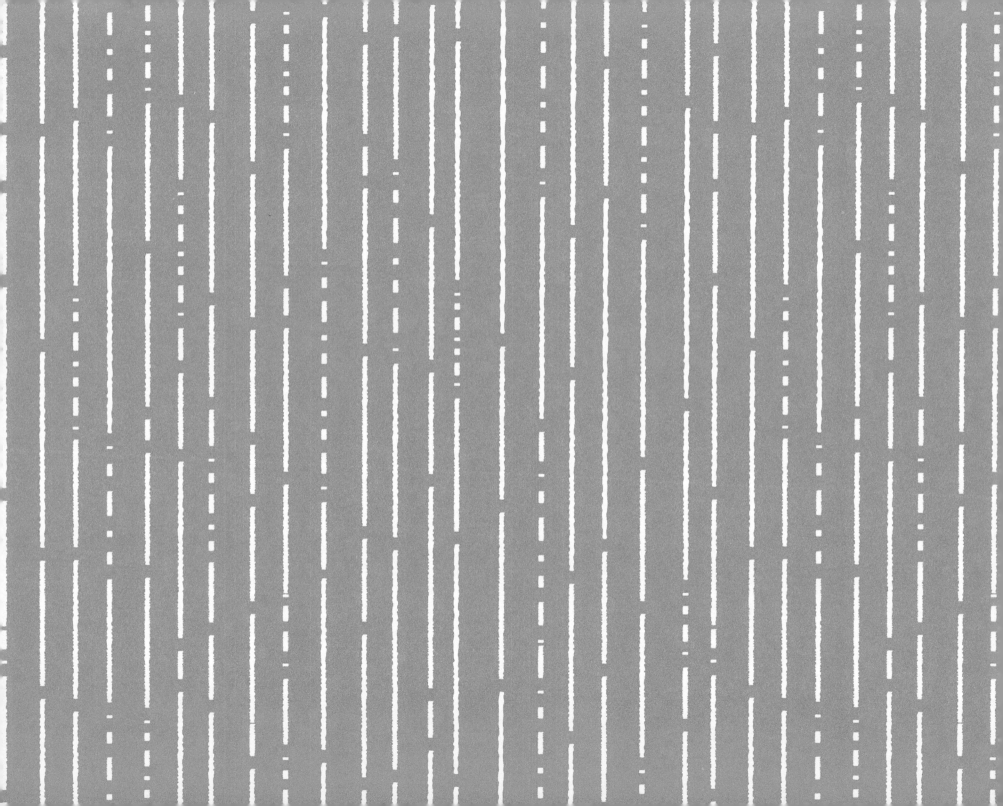

ABOUT THE AUTHOR

Linda Swindle is an artist and retired elementary school teacher.
Her paintings are filled with vivid and often unexpected color in
a loose interpretation of her subject matter.

Linda's work can be seen at Red Chair Gallery in Bend, Oregon,
The Gallery at Ten Oaks in McMinnville, Oregon, and on her website at
www.LSWatercolor.com.